Learn to Draw

MYTHICAL CREATURES

Learn to draw 10 mythical creatures in easy to follow steps.

Learn to Draw: CENTAUR

A centaur is a creature depicted as half human and half horse in Greek mythology. Centaurs are sometimes portrayed as wise and noble and sometimes they are portrayed as proud. They are skilled in archery, healing and astrology.

Step 1

Draw an oval shape for the head and a broad penaut shape for the trunk. Underneath this make a large cylinder shape for the body of the horse. Add a curved line at the back of this for the position of the tail. Use further lines to position the legs and the arms. The left arm should be pointing up and the right one down. Indicate the joints with small circles.

Step 2

Draw an ear on the right side of the centaur's head. Sketch in the arms and hands along the guide lines. Notice how the muscles of the chest and abdomen are shown. From the leg guide lines create the horse's forelegs and hind legs, making sure to outline the hooves too.

Drawing Tip

Do some research before you start to draw the feet and hooves of animals. Notice how they differ. For instance, the hoof of a horse is a different shape from that of a cow.

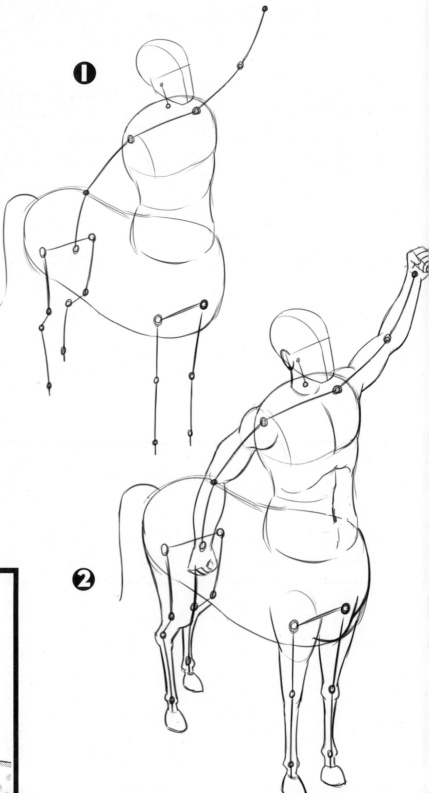

Step 3

Sketch in the hair and beard and add a sword in the centaur's left hand. Make him hold it almost parallel to his head. Fill in a bushy tail around the guide line you have already drawn.

③

Step 4

Draw in the eyes, nose and mouth and add more detail to the hair and beard. Firm up the outlines and take care to show a smooth transition from the human part of the torso into the horse's body.

④

Place the Sticker

Learn to Draw: DRAGON

The dragon is one of the most popular mythical creatures. It is found in many folk stories and legends. Dragons are like huge lizards. They have long tails and large wings. They can breathe fire!

Step 1

Draw a large oval shape for the dragon's body. Above this and slightly to the left draw a circle for the dragon's head and add two lines for the position of the mouth. Create two long curved lines to join the two. This will become the neck. At the bottom of the oval make a long curved tail. Sketch in the position of the fore and hind legs and joints.

Step 2

Add in the detail of the fore and hind legs around the guide lines. Trace the shape of a beak-like mouth and firm up the detail of the neck and tail. Note that the hind legs are much larger then the forelegs.

Drawing Tip

The more detail you put into adding reptile scales to your dragon the more realistic your drawing will look. For a more rugged look, you can add tears where your creature has gotten into a fight or two.

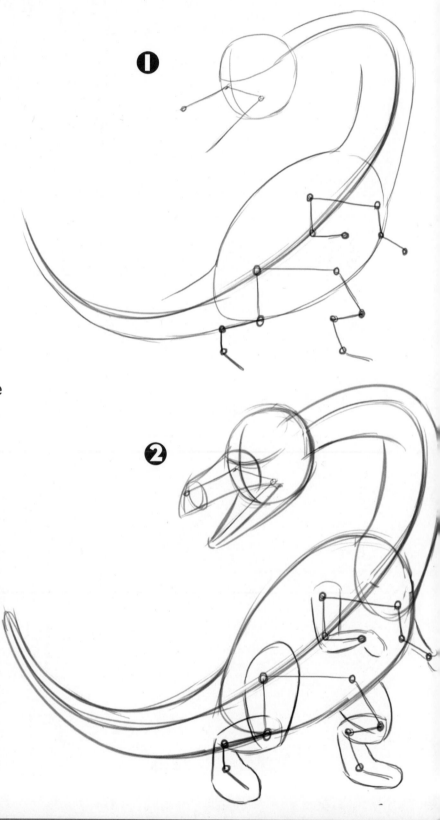

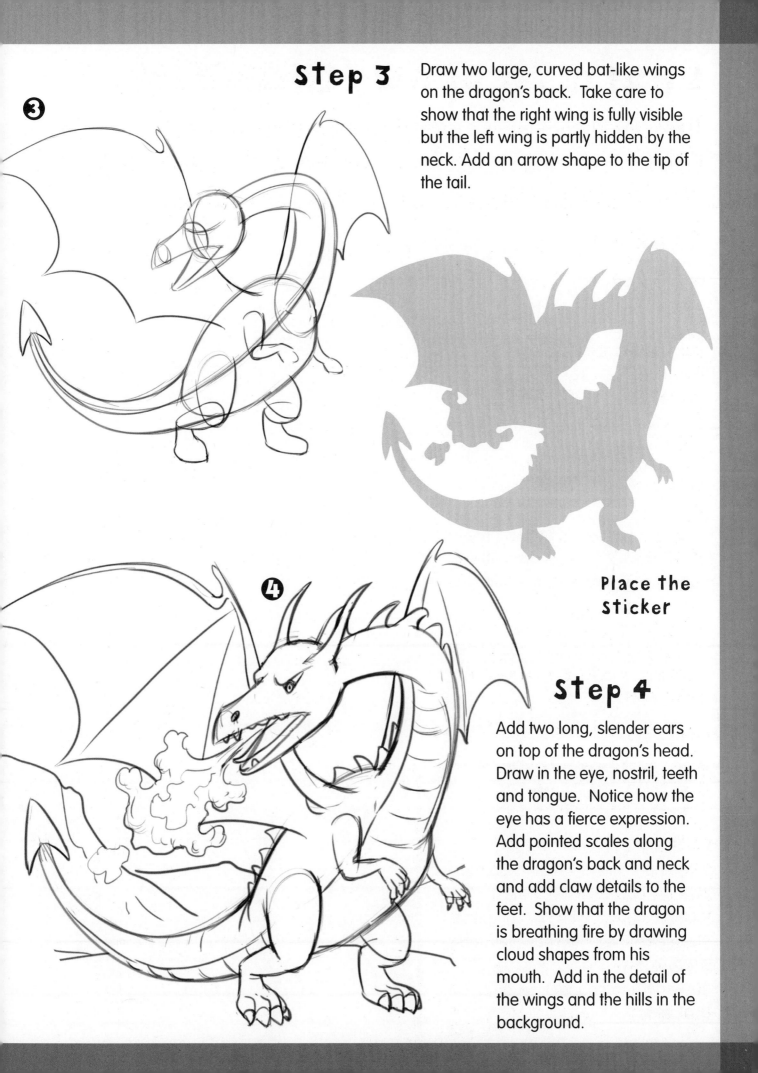

Step 3

Draw two large, curved bat-like wings on the dragon's back. Take care to show that the right wing is fully visible but the left wing is partly hidden by the neck. Add an arrow shape to the tip of the tail.

Place the Sticker

Step 4

Add two long, slender ears on top of the dragon's head. Draw in the eye, nostril, teeth and tongue. Notice how the eye has a fierce expression. Add pointed scales along the dragon's back and neck and add claw details to the feet. Show that the dragon is breathing fire by drawing cloud shapes from his mouth. Add in the detail of the wings and the hills in the background.

Learn to Draw: GIANT

A giant is a creature of superhuman size. Giants are often depicted as being cruel and wicked. They carry heavy clubs which they use as weapons. In some stories, however, they are shown to be kind.

Step 1

Draw a curved, shield shape for the head. Draw a large pillow shape, with a curve in the centre, for the giant's body. Sketch in lines for the position of the arms and legs and use dots to show the joints.

Step 2

Sketch in the giant's clothes. Draw a belt around his waist and tattered edges to his tunic sleeves. Add thick bands around his wrists. Make a v-shaped neckline and end his tunic at mid-thigh. Fill in strong arms and stout legs using the guide lines you have already drawn.

Drawing Tip

Practice the contour drawing technique. This is when you draw only the outline of the subject without starting with sketching the skeleton. It helps to show the mass and volume of the subject rather than the detail.

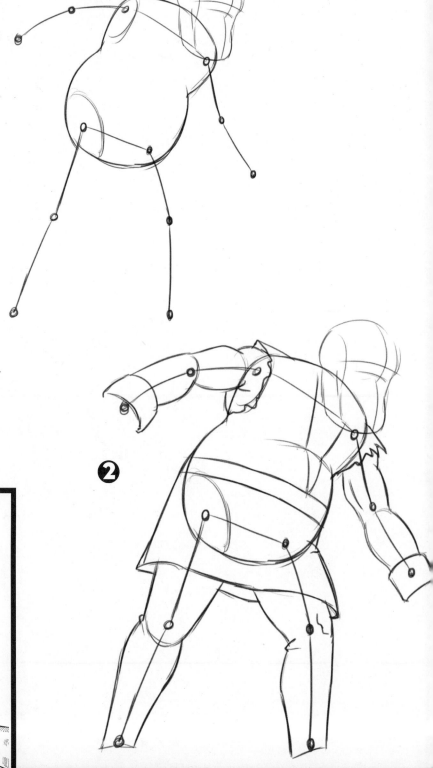

③

Step 3

Draw two large ears and add coarse hair behind them, leaving the top of his head bald. Add his hands and place a large club in his right hand. Put short boots on his feet.

Step 4

Draw the eyes, nose and mouth and use lines on the face to show his expression. Add in a line for the ground and draw two small trees below his left hand. Put lines on his clothing to show the folds and creases of the material. Add metal studs to his wrist bands. Erase any unwanted lines.

Place the Sticker

④

Learn to Draw: MINOTAUR

A creature from Greek mythology, the Minotaur has the body of a man and the head of a bull. In the myths, he was said to live inside a maze where he fought and killed anyone who tried to conquer him.

Step 1

Draw a skull shape for the Minotaur's head. Add a large, peanut-shaped body, making sure that the upper part is wider than the lower. Sketch lines for the position of the arms and legs and show the joints with dots.

Step 2

Draw curved horns either side of the head. Create the arms and legs around the lines you have already drawn. Make them strong and muscular. Add a curved line for the neck.

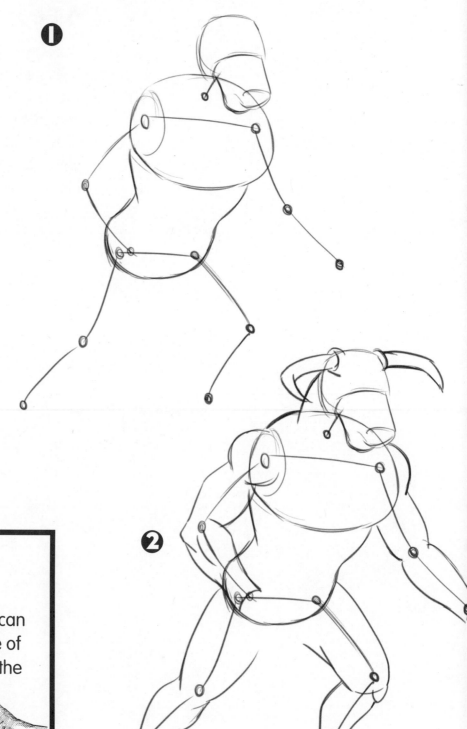

Drawing Tip

A few curved strokes and lines can help define the muscular shape of your subject. Practice drawing the biceps and defining the chest and abdominal muscles.

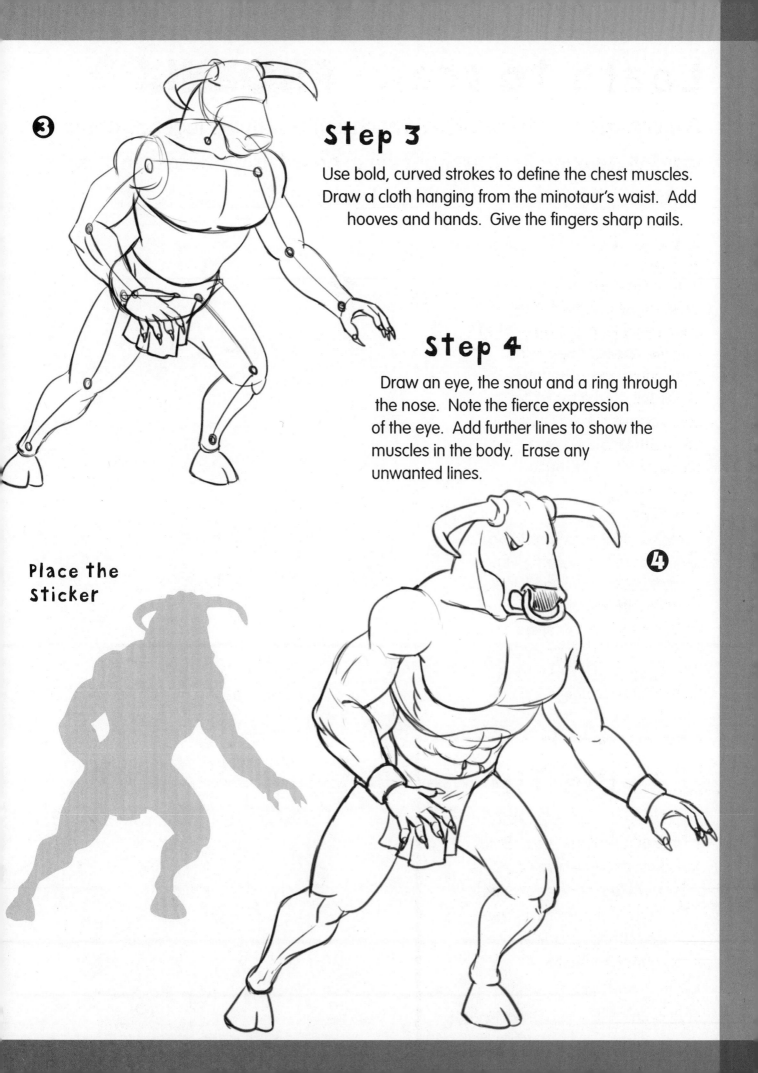

3

Step 3

Use bold, curved strokes to define the chest muscles. Draw a cloth hanging from the minotaur's waist. Add hooves and hands. Give the fingers sharp nails.

Step 4

Draw an eye, the snout and a ring through the nose. Note the fierce expression of the eye. Add further lines to show the muscles in the body. Erase any unwanted lines.

4

Place the Sticker

Learn to Draw: PHOENIX

The phoenix is a mythical bird which is found in the legends of many races. It regenerates itself from the ashes of its predecessor. It is normally shown with magnificent feathers.

Step 1

Draw a circle for the phoenix's head, an oval shape for the body and a long line connecting them for its neck. Below the body add a curved shape for the tail. At the top of the body make a curved line on each side for the wings. Add a curved beak on the head.

Step 2

Complete the wings by adding a long curve below each of the guide lines. Onto this add curly lines for the ornamental feathers. Draw curved crest feathers at the back of the head and add long thin lines below the tail. Fill out the shape of the neck.

Drawing Tip

Use different types of pencil stroke to give different textures. Bold, broad strokes will give one type of feel, while soft, irregular lines will create a different impression. Practice both to decide which techniques are best used for each of your drawings.

Step 3

Fill in the wings by drawing a repeating curve-shaped pattern along them. Do the same on the base of the tail.

Place the Sticker

Step 4

Draw the eye and add flames rising behind the phoenix. Fill out the detail of the tail feathers. Define the beak and add the phoenix's tongue. Erase any unwanted lines.

Learn to Draw: UNICORN

The unicorn has a body like a horse but has a long horn projecting from its forehead. The unicorn was believed to have the power to cure illnesses and was a symbol of purity and grace.

Step 1

Draw a long cylindrical shape in the middle of the page for the unicorn's body Higher up add a circle for the unicorn's head and add a cylinder with a rounded end on the left of it. On this sketch in the mouth with a nostril above it. Draw a curved shape for the position of the neck and add another curved line at the back of the body for the tail. Sketch in lines for the legs and position the joints.

Step 2

Using your guide lines complete the shape of the neck and legs and add on the hooves. Try to copy the posture of the unicorn to add to the character of your drawing.

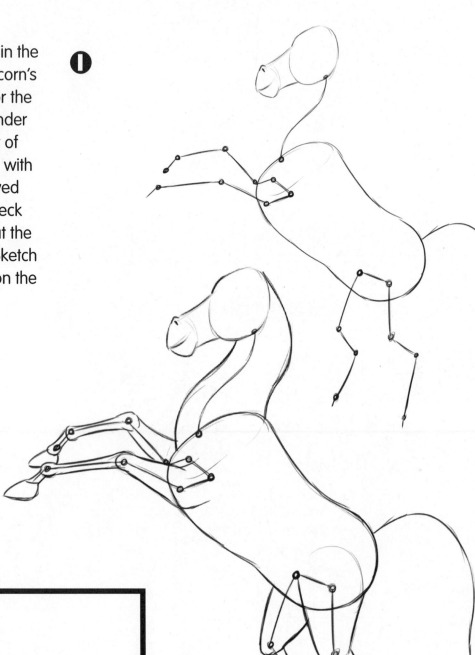

Drawing Tip

Creating bends and curves in the limbs of your subjects will help convey movement. Experiment with ways of show that a horse is galloping or a bird is about to take flight.

Step 3

Add the unicorn's ears and between them a conical horn, projecting from the forehead. Use curved lines to draw the unicorn's mane stretching from the ears to the bottom of its neck. Sketch in a long flowing tail.

Place the sticker

③

④

Step 4

Draw the unicorn's eye and firm up the mouth, nostrils and ears. Use sweeping lines on the mane and tail to create an impression of movement as the unicorn rises up. Define the legs to show the power of the muscles. Erase any unwanted lines.

Learn to Draw: VAMPIRE

A vampire is a creature which only comes out at night. During the day it sleeps in a coffin. Vampires are said to drink the blood of their victims and can turn in to bats. Count Dracula is one of the most popular vampires described in literature.

Step 1

Draw a peanut shape for the vampire's body, with a pointed skull shape for his head. The body should be roughly twice the length of the head. Add lines for the position of the arms and legs and use dots to show where the joints are.

Step 2

Sketch in the arms and trousers around the lines you have drawn. Create a long cloak with curved lines starting below the vampire's chin and passing over the arms before finishing in wavy lines on the floor. Give the cloak a high stand-up collar.

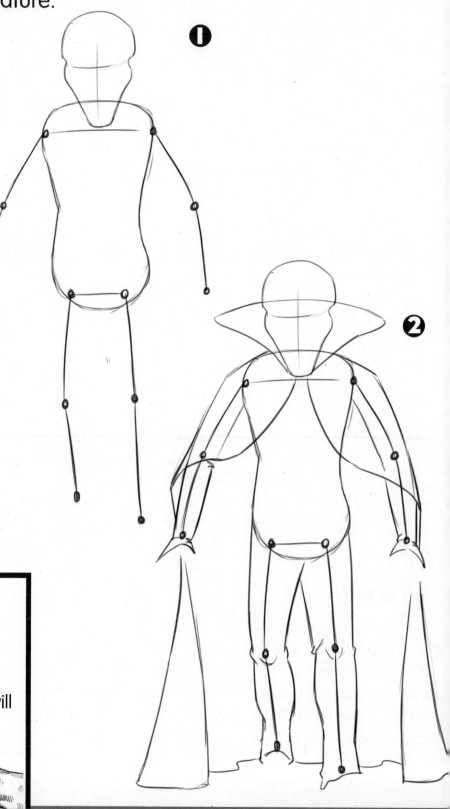

Drawing Tip

Using your own hands as a model try different angles and gestures and practice drawing them. This will help you to show different actions and emotions in the characters you draw.

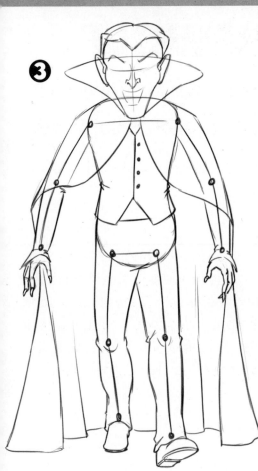

Step 3

Sketch in the hair, starting in a v shape in the centre of the forehead. Add long ears and trace in the eyebrows, a thin nose and an open mouth. Draw in the outline of the vampire's waistcoat. Draw the hands and fingers and add sharp nails. Add the shoes and make sure one foot is raised to give the impression of movement.

Step 4

Draw in the eyes and add detail to the mouth, including sharp pointed teeth. Notice how the shape of the eyes and eyebrows conveys a cruel expression. Add lines on the vampire's clothes to give the idea of folded cloth. Erase any unwanted lines.

Place the Sticker

Learn to Draw: WEREWOLF

A werewolf is a mythical creature which has the power to shape-shift from human to wolf and back again. This transformation is supposed to be triggered by the full moon.

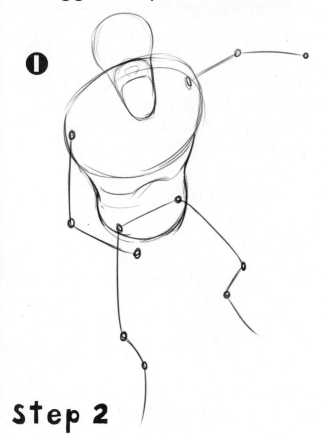

Step 1

Draw an elongated triangular head onto a cylindrical body that is broader at the shoulders and tapers around the waist. Draw lines to show the position of the arms and legs and add dots to indicate the joints. Note the position of the limbs which will help create a feeling of movement.

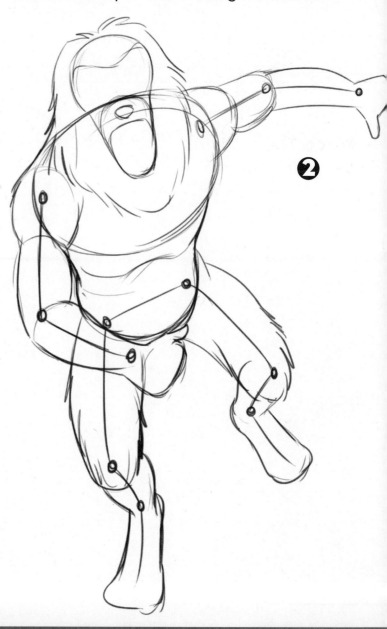

Step 2

Draw a mane round the head using soft curved strokes. Keep your strokes light to show the soft, hairy texture of the mane. Fill in the shape of the muscular arms and legs around your guide lines. Add hands and feet and show the position of the nose.

Drawing Tip

The use of pointy teeth, clawed hands and feet, wild fur and narrow frowning eyes will make your creatures look frightening.

③

Step 3

Draw two pointed ears on top of the head. Use more curved strokes to define the fur on the arms and legs. Add fingers and toes with sharp claws. Use light strokes to define the chest muscles.

Step 4

Draw the eyes and an open mouth with a set of razor sharp teeth. Notice how the shape of the eyebrows and the lines on the face help give a cruel expression and try to copy this. Add more details to the fur and then erase any unwanted lines.

④

Place the Sticker

Learn to Draw: WITCH

Witches are popular characters in legends and fairy tales. They are often shown as evil women with magical powers. They are frequently shown wearing tall pointed hats and flying on broomsticks.

Step 1

Draw and elongated skull shape for the witch's head and a curved shape for her body. Make sure the bottom end of the peanut points backwards. Draw lines for the position of the arms and legs and show the position of the joints. Be sure to copy the bends of the arms and legs.

Step 2

Draw in a long flowing gown. This should have loose sleeves and the skirt should flow out behind and below the witch's body. Use simple curved strokes on the skirt to show movement.

Drawing Tip

Experiment by taking a basic body shape and drawing it at different angles to show different actions and postures. We have used this technique here to give the illusion of flight.

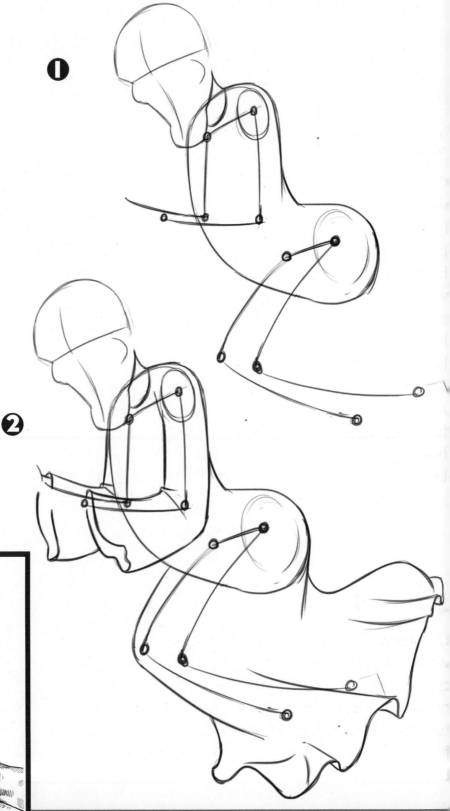

3

Place the
sticker

Step 3

Give the witch a wide-brimmed hat with a crooked point. Draw the broomstick on which the witch is sitting with a bent handle in front of her and a fluffy broom behind her. Add hands and feet. Show the hands grasping the broom handle.

4

Step 4

Use the witch's facial features to give her a wicked expression. Give her bushy eyebrows and a large, crooked nose above an open mouth. Draw long wavy hair flowing out behind her. This will help give the impression that she is flying. Firm up the details in her clothes and the broom before erasing any unwanted lines.

Learn to Draw: WIZARD

Wizards are usually shown wearing pointed hats and long flowing robes. They often have long beards and carry magic wands. A wizard has magical powers and can change people into other creatures using magic spells.

Step 1

Draw an oval shape for the wizard's head and a peanut shape for the body. Notice that for this drawing the head is placed directly on the body without showing a neck. Draw lines for the position of the arms and legs. Make sure the arms are raised above the wizard's head. Add dots to show the position of the joints.

Step 2

Draw a long conical hat, bent at the end and with a bobble. Add the outline of a flowing cloak sweeping from his shoulders to the floor. Give it wide sleeves and show an opening at the front.

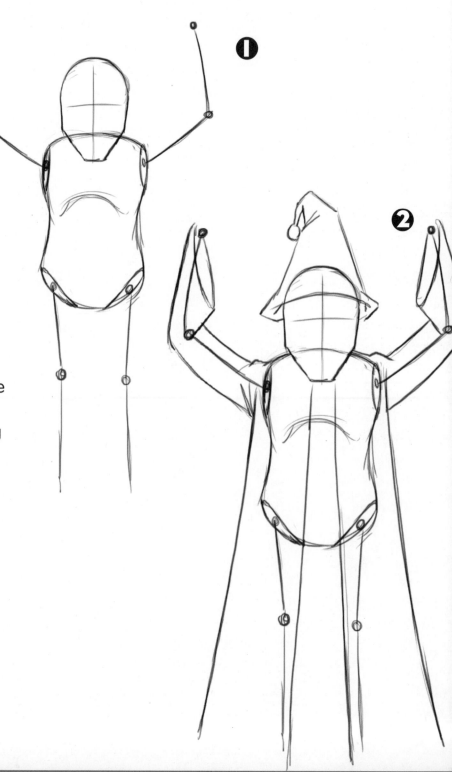

Drawing Tip

If some part of your picture cannot be erased but you want to get rid of it, try using a white gel pen instead to paint it out.

③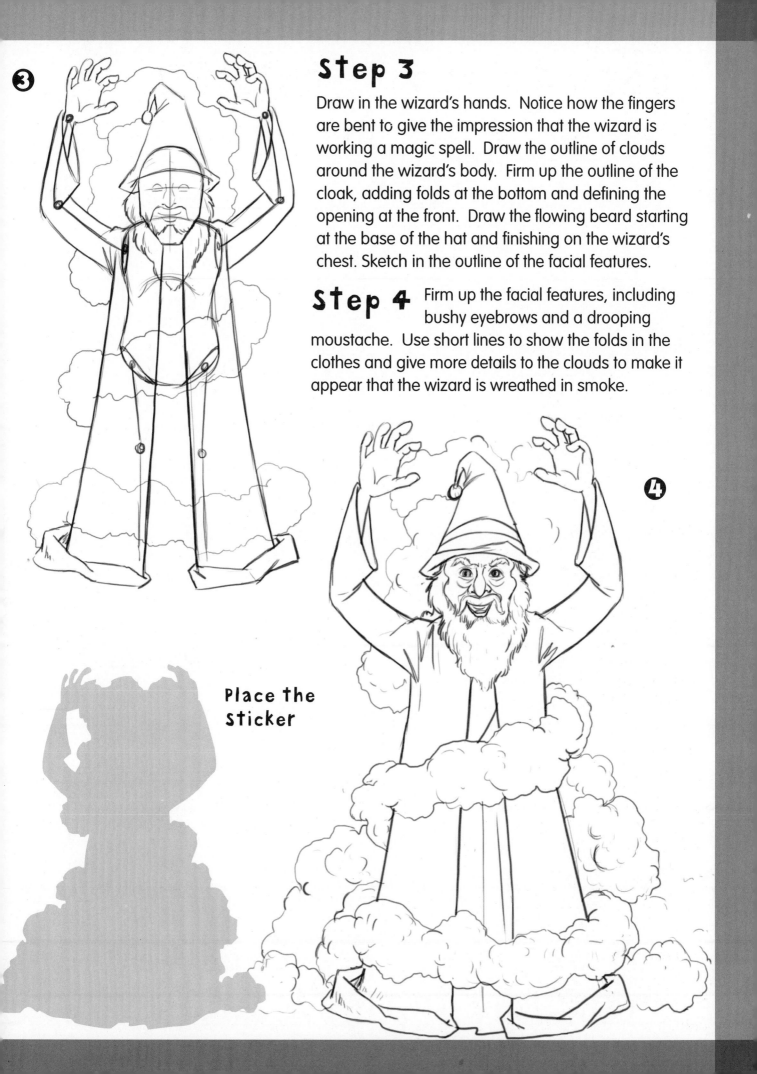

Step 3

Draw in the wizard's hands. Notice how the fingers are bent to give the impression that the wizard is working a magic spell. Draw the outline of clouds around the wizard's body. Firm up the outline of the cloak, adding folds at the bottom and defining the opening at the front. Draw the flowing beard starting at the base of the hat and finishing on the wizard's chest. Sketch in the outline of the facial features.

Step 4
Firm up the facial features, including bushy eyebrows and a drooping moustache. Use short lines to show the folds in the clothes and give more details to the clouds to make it appear that the wizard is wreathed in smoke.

❹

Place the Sticker

cut out the page opposite
and colour in the drawing

NorthParadePublishing